It's a Dog's Life

This edition published by Parragon Books Ltd in 2017

Parragon Books Ltd
Chartist House
15–17 Trim Street
Bath BA1 1HA, UK
www.parragon.com

Copyright © Parragon Books Ltd 2017

Designed by Talking Design

ISBN 978-1-4748-6929-4
Printed in China

It's a Dog's Life

Colour your favourite scene and
finish with decorative stickers

PaRragon

Bath • New York • Cologne • Melbourne • Delhi
Hong Kong • Shenzhen • Singapore

Are you barking mad for dogs?

Do you want to de-stress and add a little humour to your life? If the answer is 'yes', then this fun and quirky colouring and sticker book is just for you.

By now we all know that creative colouring is a fantastic way to reduce stress, inspire mindfulness and improve coordination and artistic skills. It's also long been established that animals can have a calming effect on our lives and improve our general happiness. Dogs, in particular, are proven to reduce stress if you play with them. So why not combine these feel-good factors in a completely new way? Just take a few moments to suspend your reality, open the pages of this book, colour away any anxieties and add zany, characterful stickers to complete the scenes.

Enjoying this book is simple. First choose an outdoor or indoor setting, ranging from a chic living room to a picnic in the park, or a circus stage to a sunny beach. Whatever your mood there's a picture to suit you. Then personalize the pages by colouring in the illustrated backgrounds or patterns to make the space your own. Finally, the three-dimensional photographic scenes provide a witty narrative for you to add your canine-themed stickers to create all sorts of crazy pictures.

Flip to the back of the book to find over 200 stickers to choose from, including playful puppies, sleepy hounds and an array of dog treats, toys and accessories to help bring the scenes to life and give your canine friends real character. Place a row of pooch stickers along the stools at a bar with cocktails in paws, dress up a pup with hat and tie in an office space, or add a playful dog and ball to a garden. You could even add a jet-setting pooch to an airport scene! Then peel the stickers off and start again.

So relax, grab your colouring pencils and unleash your canine creativity!

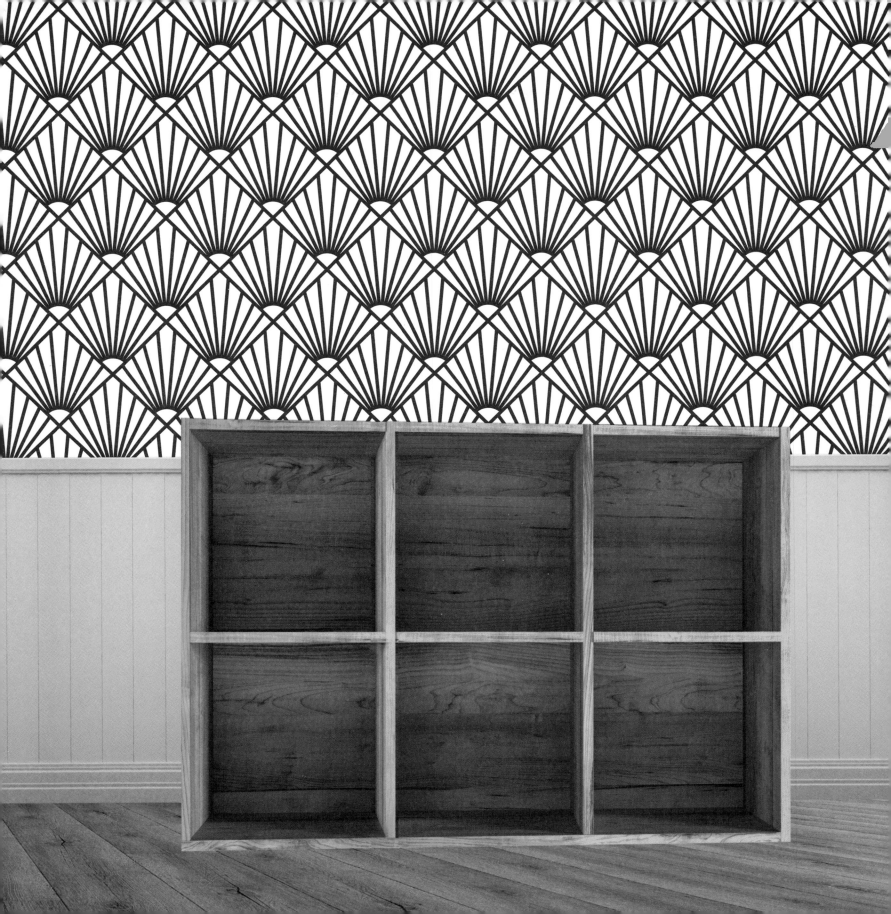

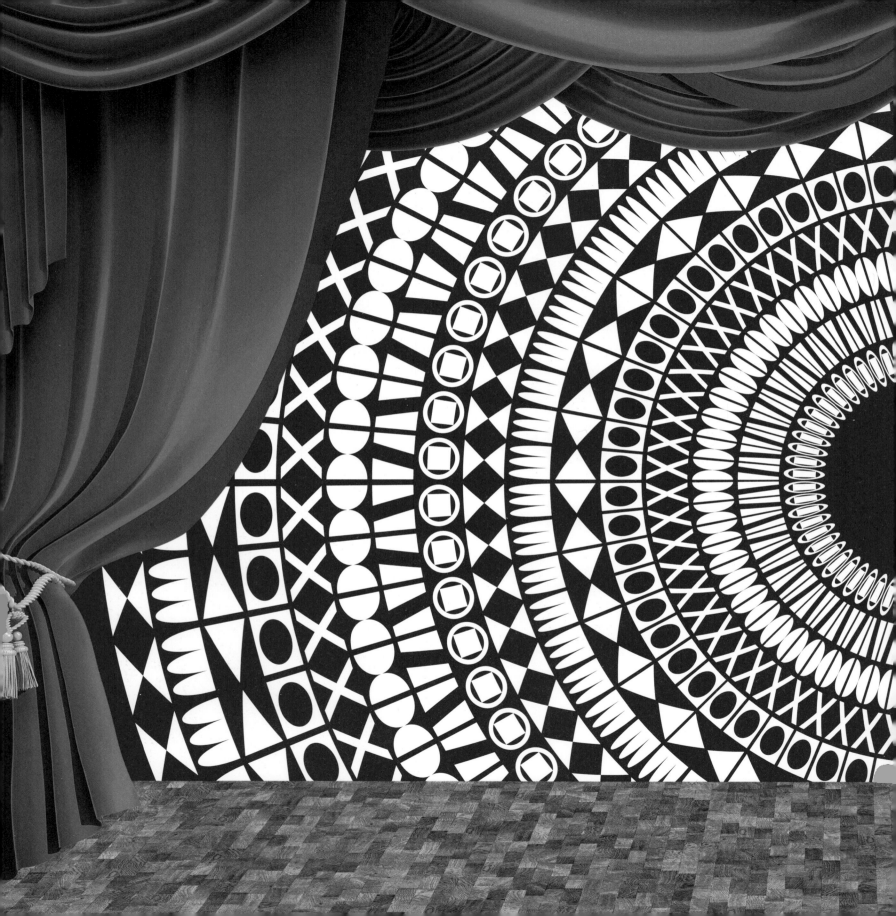

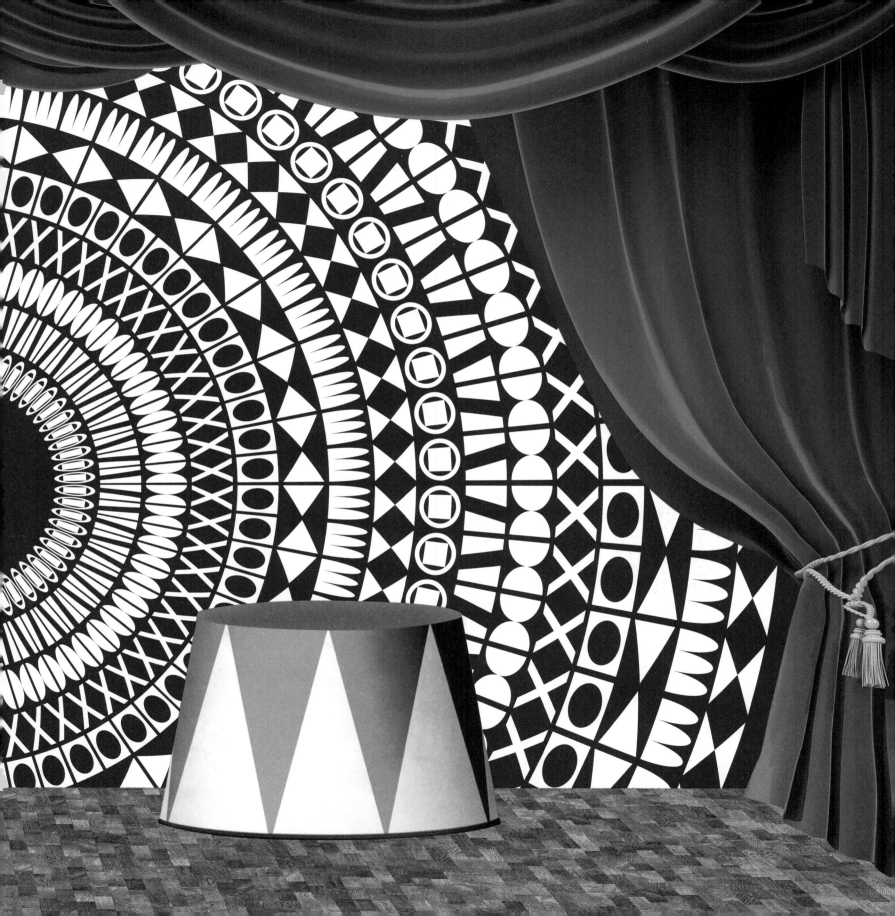